Follow the Leader

HOUGHTON MIFFLIN COMPANY

BOSTON

ATLANTA   DALLAS   GENEVA, ILLINOIS   PALO ALTO   PRINCETON

FOLLOW THE LEADER

By Kathleen Fraser

Illustrated by Hélène Desputeaux

Whatever he does, you have to do too,
because he is the leader.

When he jumps off the porch,
you have to jump too (even
when you're a little bit scared),
because he is the leader.

If he yells "blueberry" very loud
or says "hello" to a frog,
you have to do all those things,
because he is the leader.

But then his turn is over.

And you are next.

And everyone stands behind you
and waits for you to begin.

11

And they have to do
whatever silly things
you can think of,
because YOU are
the leader now.